P9-EDH-992

Snug in the Snow

by

Elizabeth Low

Illustrated by Ronni Solbert

Little, Brown and Company
BOSTON TORONTO

Books by Elizabeth Low

MOUSE, MOUSE, GO OUT OF MY HOUSE
SNUG IN THE SNOW

LIBRARY OF CONGRESS CATALOG CARD NO. 63 — 14236

FIRST EDITION

Published simultaneously in Canada
by Little, Brown & Company (Canada) Limited

PRINTED IN THE UNITED STATES OF AMERICA

To the children of Heron Hollow

Summer was over and it was time to go home. Jamie sat sadly on the steps of the cottage watching the golden leaves drift down.

"I don't see why we go away now," he said. "It's nicer here than ever before."

The maple tree was red as fire, its leaves like little flames.

"Because winter's coming, that's why," called Aunt Kate from the kitchen, where she was packing up. "Brrrh! This place is like an iceberg already, and the water will soon be freezing in the pipes. I'll have to keep it running or there will be trouble."

She opened the kitchen door. "Here, Jamie," she said in her serious voice. "Take this basket and go out to the garden. Pick whatever you see that's good to eat. There will be frost tonight, and we must not let a scrap of food go to waste. We'll take it all home with us tomorrow."

"Yes, Aunt Kate," said Jamie. But he didn't move.

The mountain glowed with bright colors and the waves went slap-slap against the sandy shore.

"Hurry, now. It will soon be dark!" said Aunt Kate.

"All right."

Still Jamie didn't move. How soft the path was with fallen pine needles! The family had gone home, all but the two of them. Jamie had asked to stay over to help his aunt close up the summer cottage for the winter.

Yet he didn't move.

Aunt Kate stood staring up at the gray sky.

"My, I wouldn't like to be caught up here in this cold cabin and not be able to get home," she said, shivering. "I declare, it looks like snow!"

Then Jamie jumped.

"Oh, boy!" he thought. "If it should snow, we might not go! We might get snowed in, or something."

Jamie lived most of the year in the South, where it hardly ever snows. He was always wishing for snow. He wanted to be out in a snowstorm more than anything else in the world.

"How do you know, Aunt Kate?" he asked, as quietly as he could.

His aunt looked up and all about her, and shook her head.

"Some kind of storm is threatening, Jamie. I feel it in my bones. I can't tell you how. But you are as good a weatherman as I am. Smell the wind, study the sky, remember the moon. What do *you* say?" She laughed a little, to sound cheerful. "Be off with you now, and fill up that basket."

She turned and went quickly inside, murmuring, "I don't like the look of it at all."

Jamie stood up straight.

"She says you can feel it in your bones," he was thinking. He drew a long breath and tried to feel his bones.

He was not sure he felt anything special.

He held a wet forefinger to the wind, which blew lightly out of the northwest. He stared up at the darkening sky, iron-colored now, and he saw no moon or star.

He made up his mind.

"It sure smells snowy," he whispered. "Please come, snow."

Then he ran down the path toward the garden. He stopped once, raising his head to the cool evening air.

"When it comes," he wondered, "does it feel speckly and tingly, like rain? Or soft, like feather brushes on your face?"

He ran on, but suddenly had a different idea. He turned off the path into the high grass, toward a spot where the wild grapevines twined up around a tall poplar tree.

Darkness was falling fast and the wind was rising. He spied the big yellow leaves of the grapevine shaking in the upper air. He climbed on an old stump and stretched up to pick the little bunches of black grapes.

Then he stopped, waiting, listening, staying stock-still. Out of the corner of his eye he had seen a shadow stirring, deep in the brushwood. It was a round dark shape that moved without a sound. There was another near it, and another, and another, all of them melting away now, into the thicket, noiselessly. Then they were gone.

They were the partridges.

Jamie loved them best of all the creatures of the fields. He had watched them often since finding the mother partridge's nest in the grass right near the path, in early summer. He had seen her guarding and teaching her young. Now the baby

partridges had grown so it was hard to tell them from their mother. They were so soft and brown and round and puffy—so quick to move and hide. Yet they were clumsy in flight, compared to other birds. They seemed to hate to leave the ground. They felt safer there.

Jamie had sat on that very stump one day for hours, watching the mother partridge lead her little ones to an anthill to feed. They pecked away hungrily as though they would never have enough! He knew they liked seeds and all kinds of berries, too.

He noticed scratchy marks on the sandy ground below him, the partridges' footprints. A few half-eaten grapes lay scattered among them.

Jamie lowered his hand from the high vine. He thought a moment, then stretched up again, higher, as high as he could reach. He tore handfuls of the grape clusters from their wiry stems. He pulled the upper tendrils of the vine off the tree trunk, filled his pockets with the grapes. Then he climbed down and spread the grapes on the sand, and put a heap of them in a hollow made by a big double root of the old stump.

"It's a mystery to me," he was thinking all the time, "how those partridges find anything to eat in the winter, under the deep snowdrifts. It's a

mystery to me. Anyway, I can find plenty of other things to fill my basket with."

He ran to the edge of the garden. There, in one corner by the cornstalks, a little animal like a gray muff was sitting, husking an ear of late corn. It was the raccoon, an old friend of Jamie's.

It sniffed the air, dropped the corn and ran to the maple tree. It was up the tree in a twinkling.

"Thanks for the idea," thought Jamie. "I'll fill my basket with corn. It makes good popcorn."

He began to gather it. The raccoon watched from a crotch in the tree.

"That little funny-face can go down to the lake and fish if he's hungry. I've seen him do that. He'll be all right this winter," Jamie decided.

His basket was almost full now. He remembered his fireplace down home, and how all the family liked to pop corn over the coals, and the toasty smell of it.

He started back toward the cottage. But after a few steps he stopped with a sigh.

"Of *course*, the lake will freeze over soon, so raccoons can't fish very well. Shucks."

Slowly he returned to the garden. He dumped his basketful of corn on the ground.

"That old 'coon will find it here, all right," he said to himself. "I'll look for something else."

His eyes swept over the whole garden. What was left to look for? The catbirds had cleaned up the blackberries. There was hardly an apple left on the apple tree. There was nothing in sight but a few old cabbage leaves, and Jamie did not care for cabbages.

His ears were cold. The damp wind seemed to go right through him. Darkness was everywhere. Even the sky seemed closer, as though it was gathering in around him. Everything felt changy, heavy, strange, and very chill.

Jamie shivered, but not from the cold. Was this the way it felt before a snowstorm? This night might be different from any night he had ever lived! Only, why did Aunt Kate seem so worried? Was it because the water pipes might freeze and burst and they would have no water to drink? Was it because they might have to put off

going home? Of course he wanted to get home to Mother and Dad, naturally. Why couldn't he? What could happen?

Aunt Kate had said that Mr. Tyler, their nearest neighbor, four miles away, had promised to call for them very early the next morning to drive them to the station in his jeep. It was all arranged.

Their bags were already packed; Jamie had even carried two big boxes out to the barn entrance near the road, to load into the jeep.

"I want it to snow, all right, but I want to get home, too," he thought. Did it make sense that Aunt Kate wanted to leave before the storm? She was a good sport, Aunt Kate was. Not afraid of garter snakes, or garden spiders, or tipping over in the canoe, the way some kids' aunts were. Why was she worried now?

"I'll tell her not to put her worrying-cap on,"

he decided. "Well, my basket's as empty as when I started out. I better get busy. Maybe I can find some mint or something on the beach."

It was very dark, but Jamie knew his way. Crows cawed overhead. The cottages and cabins around the lake were closed and there were no lights in their windows. Everyone had gone home. It was black and still and lonesome.

"Garroom!"

Jamie jumped a foot, the sound was so loud.

"Gullagarroom!"

It came again, quite near him, from the ferns at his feet. It made him catch his breath.

"Maybe I better be going," he whispered. He turned and started to run toward the cottage.

Then he made himself stop. What was there to be afraid of? It must be some wild animal, and the animals were his friends.

He stood and waited for the awful sound to come again.

"Garroom! Gullagarroom!"

Now Jamie knew—it was his friend the bullfrog, sounding much, much louder than usual.

"Hey, bullfrog! I can't see you but I know you're there," he called out bravely.

A small dark shape sprang into the air right in front of him and with a splash disappeared under the black water.

Was the bullfrog going down under because he knew a storm was on the way? "He has probably gone down, down, down in the soft black ooze where it's cozy and quiet for his winter snooze." Jamie had made up a rhyme without meaning to.

"At least I think he must have. It sounded as though he said, 'Better come along, better come

along!' No *thank* you! I've got to find some mint. It must be close to where I am. I think I smell it."

Jamie felt among the weeds and pebbles at the water's edge until his hand touched the little bushy sprays. Soon he had the bottom of his basket lined with them.

His fingers were numb with cold and he put one hand in a pocket to warm it. He wished he could find one more thing, at least, to add to his basket. Mint was not very filling, really.

"Jamie? Where *are* you?"

It was Aunt Kate, standing in the light of the kitchen window, holding a kerchief around her shoulders.

"Coming!" he called. Now he didn't want to go in. He didn't want to be warm. It was exciting out in the night.

"I'll stop for a few hickory nuts," he thought. "I bet I can find some, even in the dark."

He headed for the house and the tall shagbark hickory tree beside the stone wall. He rummaged among the dead leaves under the tree, searching for the hard, sticky outer shells of the nuts.

There was a shrill chatter over his head and bits of shell fell on his shoulder. The red squirrel was cracking a nut to get at the meat, flinging the husks through the air. Jamie dodged.

"*You* still out?" he thought, very surprised.

The wide-awake squirrel flung down the last crumbs of the shell and Jamie heard his chatter fade away in the high branches. Jamie knew where his nest was, he had watched him build it. A cold, blowy place it looked, too.

"I never saw *him* out so late," Jamie thought. "He must believe that winter's coming fast. Well, he won't need *all* those nuts. I'll take some and leave some."

He scooped up a handful and dropped them in his basket.

On the path going toward the house he felt a quick little tickle on his sneaker. It was his friend the chipmunk. Even that tiny creature was hurrying tonight! When Jamie looked along the stone wall there he was, sitting on his special flat stone nibbling something with fast jerky bites.

"Probably the rose hips again," thought Jamie. "They taste terrible, but I guess he likes the seeds. He's certainly working overtime! It's way past his bedtime. He must have winter on his mind, too."

Jamie moved quietly nearer. He picked a few hickory nuts out of his basket and placed them near the stone.

The chipmunk did not even turn his head. He tucked a seed in his cheek pouch and then ran along the wall and dove down between the stones.

Jamie walked toward the door. He was puzzled.

"He doesn't like the thought of snow, I bet," he was thinking. "He's terribly afraid of winter. He doesn't *want* it to come yet."

He stood still a moment, trying to figure it out.

"If it snows, will all the animals' food get lost and covered up so they can't find it?"

Now he didn't know *what* he wanted!

"I should think a small snowstorm would not hurt anybody," he decided, at last. "So I could have a glimpse of it."

When he showed Aunt Kate his almost empty basket, she looked disappointed.

"I had to leave a few little things for the animals to eat this winter," he said to her.

"Yes, of course," she answered. "I don't blame you one bit." But she took one last worried look at the dark sky and closed the kitchen door. "The only thing is, Jamie, if there *should* be a really bad storm and we couldn't get out for a while, we haven't much food on hand for ourselves! We have some good leftovers for supper, and cereal and one egg and a little milk for breakfast. Nothing else! Nothing else but scraps!"

Jamie pulled open one of the drawers.

"What's this?" he asked, peering at a row of small cans.

"Spices," said Aunt Kate, "I leave them here all winter. 'Sugar and spice, they are all very nice' but—" She shook her head.

"They don't fill you up," said Jamie.

Aunt Kate was looking in the flour tin. "A few scrapings," she said. "And here's a little shortening."

Jamie did not know what shortening was, but

it did not sound like much, and anyway he was wondering about something different. Had he done right to leave the corn and nuts out there for his animals?

"I know," he said. "If the snow is very deep tomorrow and we get *very* hungry, I could go out in the morning and borrow back a few things, maybe."

Aunt Kate nodded and said yes, that was a good plan. "The truth is, it's not sensible to face a snowstorm up in this country without a full cupboard. Your little wild friends could tell us that."

She turned to the stove and began to prepare supper.

Jamie stood by the window, thinking. There was one thing he could still do, one place where he had not looked thoroughly. He decided to go there.

"I'll be right back, Aunt Kate," he called over his shoulder. He ran outdoors again, this time up toward the apple tree.

He knew the tree well, even in the dark. His feet and hands found the familiar branches, like the rungs of a ladder. In a few seconds he was up near the top, feeling around gently to see if he could find one last apple that he and Dad had missed when they gathered the apples, weeks ago. He knew that on the wide-spreading branches

down below there wasn't a single apple left.

His fingers touched something smooth and round and cold. An overripe apple fell easily into his hand. He put it in his pocket. He kept on feeling in every direction but found no more. Probably that was the very last apple on the tree! He waited, staying perfectly still for a while, because it was fun to be up there high in the apple tree so late, so in the dark, so all alone.

Then he peered down, feeling for the place to put his foot. Suddenly he knew he was not alone. He drew a quick breath, and stopped moving.

Two deer, a doe and a fawn, were underneath the tree. The slender doe stretched as far up as she could reach, searching with her nose for an apple to eat.

Her little one watched, ever near.

Jamie didn't breathe or move a hair.

The doe walked calmly, slowly, around the circle of low branches. Nothing but a few dry yellow leaves. She searched on the ground. Still nothing. She found no fruit. Then, with a bound, she leaped away into the darkness and was gone, her little one right behind her.

She had not made a sound.

Jamie did not move. He was seeing the picture all over again in his mind.

"Oh! If I hadn't *luckily* looked down I wouldn't have known they came!" he thought. He gave himself a shake. Then, quickly, he began to look for more apples. He reached a little higher, he stretched a few inches farther, he bent toward himself some slender branches whose ends he could not reach, and yes, his hand struck a cluster of three small apples! He broke them from their stems and stowed them inside his jacket. Then he climbed down. Without any hesitation he scattered all four apples on the ground below the branch where the doe had first come.

Then he ran inside.

Aunt Kate looked into his face but asked no questions.

"Supper's ready!" she said, and they sat down. As they were finishing the last piece of bread, the last slice of meat, the last potato they had in the house, Jamie told her about the deer.

"And before I knew it they were gone!" he said. "They just faded away in the air!" Then

he added slowly, "I suppose that deer get hungrier than anybody in winter. They can't curl up in little holes with piles of nuts and things they've stored away, can they?"

"No," said Aunt Kate.

"So I left the apples," said Jamie.

"Of course," said Aunt Kate. "I would have done the same."

Silently, Jamie finished his good warm meal. He was thinking about what might be going to happen. He was feeling something in his bones.

When he awoke in the morning there was a ghostly light in his room and a strange sound. Jamie lay listening. He heard tiny tappings, so tiny they were hardly sounds at all.

He jumped up and looked out his window. Everything was white.

It was snowing, softly snowing, with big flakes, like torn bits of paper slowly falling, blowing sidewise, falling everywhere, falling through the air.

"Oh, boy!" whispered Jamie, hugging himself. "Boy, oh boy!"

In no time he was dressed and creeping quietly downstairs, for he was the only one awake. He opened the door and stepped into the snow.

He walked in a white land, so bright it made him blink his eyes.

He lifted his head; the flakes were soft, like little feather brushes on his face.

The white river of snow flowed everywhere—down over the sloping bank, and up the tree trunks. The tall hemlocks bent low with swoop-

ing skirts. The bushes were made of strips of soft white fur.

The fence had pillows on it and the high weeds had snowy blossoms. The snowflakes on the red and orange leaves of the maple tree were like little nets over lighted lanterns.

The whole world was alight and beautiful.

Jamie forgot everything except to be the first to step in smooth white places, and to reach out and touch the coldness, and taste the fresh flakes on his tongue.

A gust of wind blew a cloud of snow whooshing down from the roof, and cold snow dust tickled down his neck. Then it was still again.

The kitchen door burst open and Aunt Kate was calling, "Mr. Tyler . . . soon . . . tell me when you see him . . ."

Jamie hardly heard her words. He had forgotten about going home and now he wanted to stay more than ever. But there was a sharp sound down the road, which grew louder and louder. It was a beating, bangy sort of sound, like an enormous clock ticking very fast and loud. In another minute Mr. Tyler's green jeep pulled up at the front gate.

But instead of Mr. Tyler, his helper Ralph hopped down from the car.

"Morning, Jamie," he called. "Can you beat this snow, coming so early? They say it will likely get worse before it gets better. Radio says it's real bad up north. Your aunt inside? I got a message for her from Mr. Tyler."

He strode to the kitchen door. Jamie saw Aunt Kate with her coat and hat on, talking to him on the doorstep.

Hooray! He had a few minutes more! He grabbed a cold handful of snow and packed the first snowball he had ever made in his life. He aimed at a fence post, missed, and flung another, and another. He ran down to the lakeside and shot a dozen snowballs into the black water. His fingers were red and tingling.

Then he was surprised to hear the kitchen door

shut with a bang. He saw Ralph hurry out to his car alone and drive away.

"Good!" he thought. "I guess we don't have to go just yet."

He walked to the edge of the dock, which had white cushions on its crossboards. This was where Jamie dived when he went swimming.

"I wouldn't like to dive from here today. No,

sir!" He shook his almost freezing fingers. "Maybe I better go in and see if anything happened."

Inside, he found Aunt Kate with her coat still on, but she had taken off her hat. She was starting to build a fire in the fireplace, and was trying to break a piece of kindling over her knee.

"Well, Jamie, what do you think?" Her voice made Jamie feel excited.

"What?"

"How would you like to stay over for another day?"

At first Jamie couldn't speak for joy. "Oh, boy! *Can* we?"

"It looks like it. Ralph says the trains aren't running from the north because of the blizzard. Besides, Mr. Tyler's wife has taken sick and Ralph is on his way now to get the doctor for her. He says he's never seen Mr. Tyler so upset.

But he sent word by Ralph that he would come by for us tomorrow morning, if Mrs. Tyler's better and the trains are running again. So here we are!"

The stick of kindling split with a crack over Aunt Kate's knee. She leaned down to arrange the pieces over some crumpled paper.

"Boy!" whispered Jamie to himself. He could hardly believe his good fortune.

"I told Ralph we were short of food," Aunt Kate went on. "He's got to work on the road all day, but he promised to stop by toward evening. He won't forget us, I'm sure of that."

"We'll be O.K.," said Jamie. "We'll tighten our belts, like pioneers. I'd better bring in some more wood."

"Better bring the big shovel, too," said Aunt Kate. "I'll see if I can find some boots and warm things to wear. Dear me, 'most everything is put away."

Aunt Kate had a number of jobs for Jamie. Besides them, he had a hundred things to do with the snow! He went to explore the woods beyond the empty cottage next door. He listened to the strange deep silence of the snow among the tall hemlock trees. He thought of the living creatures underneath it.

"You'd never guess anyone was there!" he thought.

He *seemed* to be alone in a land where he had never been before. But he knew he wasn't.

Aunt Kate unpacked her camera, and from sheltered nooks they took pictures of everything that delighted them. When Aunt Kate went inside, Jamie stayed out a little longer. The mound of snow beside the path he had cleared looked

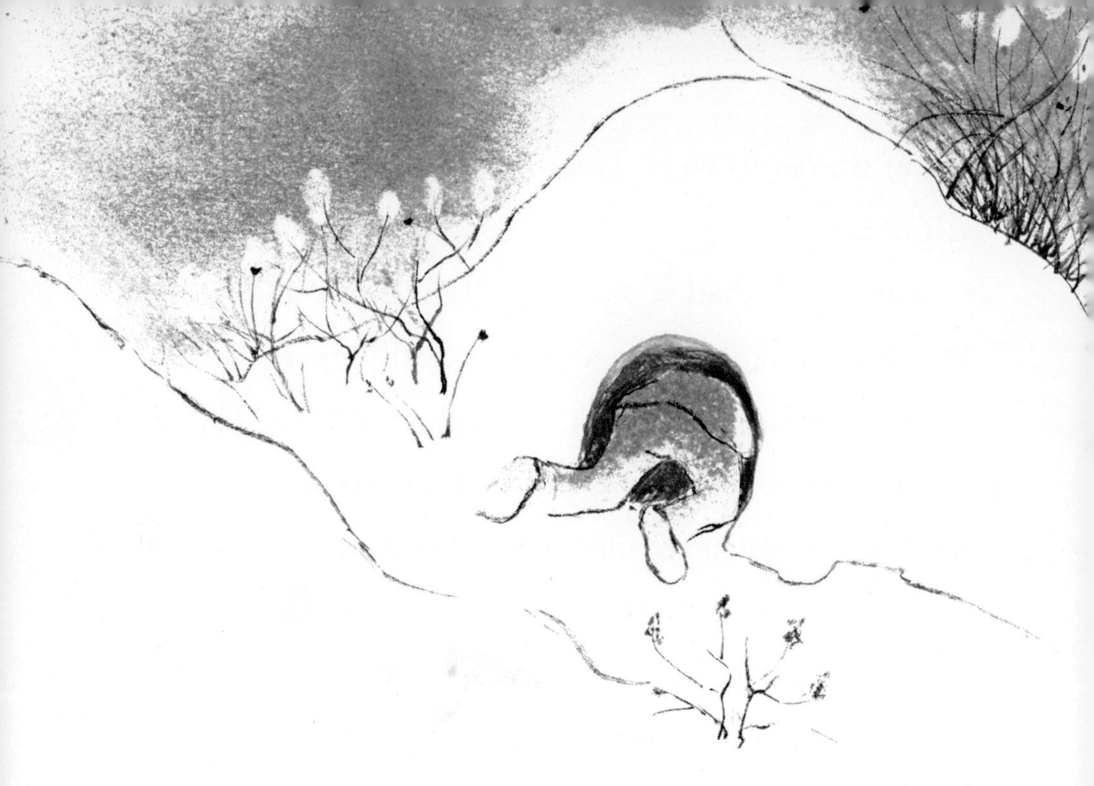

like an igloo, and he had to make a door in it and creep inside.

When at last he went into the house the sky was darker gray. The snowflakes were smaller but still falling steadily. Jamie was out of breath, tired all through, hungry as a bear.

The kitchen and living room were empty. He heard Aunt Kate's step upstairs. He stamped the

snow off his boots, loosened his coat, and looked around the kitchen. Aunt Kate had put the egg out in a saucer and the little ration of milk beside it. Jamie's basket was in a corner with the wilted mint in the bottom. The kitchen didn't seem natural.

"It smells so bare," he thought sadly.

He slumped down on a stool.

"It's my fault," he said to himself. "I bet Aunt Kate is hungry, too. I certainly should not have left all that food out there for my animals. I've got to do *something*."

With a sigh he fastened up his coat and went out of doors.

Aunt Kate heard the door close. She looked out of the upper window and watched Jamie as he went slowly out toward the snow-covered garden.

Then, he turned suddenly and with a leap

started running as fast as the snow would let him, with high long steps, up toward the barn entrance by the road. She soon lost sight of him behind the veil of new falling snow.

When she went downstairs a few moments later he had come in so quietly she had not heard him.

He was sitting on the kitchen stool with a big grin on his face.

He didn't say a word. He just watched her as her eyes swept over the empty counters. She walked toward the stove. There, beside the little dish with the lonely egg and the milk, was a big round glowing orange pumpkin!

"Oh, Jamie!" said Aunt Kate with a gasp.

Jamie sat there like a Cheshire cat, with his shoulders hunched up, his eyes twinkling. He knew they were both thinking the same thing.

The dream of a spicy rich pumpkin pie was in their minds, and both of them knew it.

This was the pumpkin Jamie had planted and raised by himself, and he had packed it up to take home with him to Texas. It was a large pumpkin and a fine one, and Jamie was very fond of it because he had watched it grow. He had taken it up to the barn two days ago with their other extra luggage, ready to load into the car.

"And I had forgotten all about it!" sighed Aunt Kate happily. "Jamie, I believe you've saved the day!"

With a smile as big as Jamie's she pulled the lid off the flour tin, opened the spice drawer, lit the oven, and rolled up her sleeves.

Jamie handed her the wooden rolling pin. Then he went in to warm his toes beside the fire and wait.

It was not long before the first sweet smell of spice blew in from the kitchen. Soon the whole room was full of fragrance. Then the pie was out of the oven and on a little table between them in front of the fire, golden, warm, and delicious to behold.

It was a beautiful, beautiful pie, big and melting and sweet-tasting and very filling. They each ate three pieces.

Snowflakes tapped on the windowpanes and the fire crackled brightly. How warm and cosy it was to be inside looking out.

"I believe the pie tastes better because of the snow," said Aunt Kate.

Jamie nodded. "And maybe the snow looks even more magical because we're full of pie," he said, laughing.

There was no sound from the empty road. No one came by all afternoon. Jamie and his aunt played parchesi, as they often had before. By evening the snow stopped, and just at dark Ralph stamped down the path past the barn and knocked at the door.

He brought news that Mr. Tyler's wife was better, and that the trains were running again. He believed the storm was over. He had gotten stuck on the hill in a snowdrift and he couldn't get to market. But he pulled two paper bags out of his pockets and set them on the kitchen shelf.

"Here's a quart of milk and a loaf of bread," he said. "I borrowed them from Mrs. Adams when I stopped at the depot to ask about trains." Mr. Adams was the stationmaster, and the Adamses lived right by the station.

"Tisn't much, but it will likely tide you over," he said, as he left.

Aunt Kate and Jamie thanked Ralph and ate bread and milk for supper, and the last of their pie. The next morning, when Jamie woke, he heard dripping sounds from the roof over his windowsill. The snow was melting.

"That little droppy is singing a tune," he whispered to himself. He lay and listened to the music, smiling. Then he jumped up and looked out on the snowy white world that looked so safe and bright.

They ate the rest of their bread and milk for breakfast. Soon afterward Mr. Tyler drove up in his rattly jeep, full of good cheer and the news that Mrs. Tyler was feeling "chipper" and the trains were running almost "regular" again.

Aunt Kate put on her hat and scurried around getting ready to leave.

"Here, let me give you a hand with that luggage," said Mr. Tyler, and tramped up to his car with his arms full of bags. Jamie quickly put on his coat and followed him. When he reached the road Mr. Tyler was underneath his car, working on the broken chain which, he said, made his jeep sound like a clock.

"Reckon I've got just time to mend this old chain," he said, cheerfully, pulling wire and a pair of pincers out of his pocket. "Darn thing keeps breaking in a new place every time I look at it."

Jamie leaned over to watch. He had never seen chains before, and were they interesting! Mr. Tyler worked quickly, talking all the time.

"Mrs. Tyler sent you over some popcorn to take home," he said to Jamie. "So you see she's herself again!"

Aunt Kate came out and climbed into the front seat, all smiles. "We'll have to stay up here all winter some year, won't we, Jamie? We'll get your dad to put a furnace in the house! Have we plenty of time, Mr. Tyler?"

"Just one minute, ma'am. You hold your horses."

Jamie answered both people at once. "Oh, thanks, Mr. Tyler. You bet, Aunt Kate." He took a last look at the snow-covered meadow. He wished he knew for *certain* what had happened to his wild friends. Would they *surely* find that food in this snow?

Mr. Tyler, still on his knees beside the wheel, was twisting a new bit of wire.

Jamie wanted terribly to watch, but he wanted to see something else more.

"Right back!" he called over his shoulder.

Which place? There was only time for one.

He knew. He waded through the snow to the poplar tree where the ragged grapevine hung. He found the old stump, though it hardly showed in its robe of white. He crouched down by the place where the big double root must be, and thrust his hand into the cold snow. He dug out three or four handfuls, and finally felt the sandy place on the ground where he had piled the grapes.

The sand was bare.

The grapes were gone.

From where he knelt he could look right and left, through the low branches of the thicket. He saw small quiet caverns with white roofs,

like halls, sheltered from the wind and almost bare of snow.

Way, way in, under the farthest branch, there were dusky shadows, huddling safe and warm. Jamie was quite sure they were partridges, gathered close, not a bit afraid.

"They're pretty safe!" he thought. "It's like

a house with little rooms. They found those grapes all right."

"All aboard!" called Mr. Tyler.

Jamie ran to the jeep. As they drove off over the one-track road, the chains held. There was only the sound of the steady chugging motor.

A swirl of leaves skittered over the smooth snow like tumbleweed on the prairie.

"There won't be any food going to waste around here. It will be all eaten up, every scrap!" he said to himself. "I'm glad I left it there! My animals won't be hungry this winter. They'll be snug, snug, snug in the snow!"